GARDENER'S RECORD BOOK

GARDENER'S RECORD BOOK

ANTONY ATHA

LORENZ BOOKS

Photographs in the book were taken by; Peter Anderson, Michelle Garrett, Jacqui Hurst,
Lucy Mason and Debbie Patterson. Additional pictures supplied by
Peter McHoy on pp 30, 31, 41, 42, 44, 52, 53 and 54

This edition first published in 1998 by Lorenz Books
27 West 20th Street, New York, NY 10011

LORENZ BOOKS are available for bulk purchase for sales promotion and for premium use.
For details, write or call the sales director,
Lorenz Books, 27 West 20th Street, New York, NY 10011; (800) 354-9657

© 1997 Anness Publishing Limited

Lorenz Books is an imprint of Anness Publishing Limited

ISBN 1 85967 347 3

Written and researched by: Antony Atha
Publisher: Joanna Lorenz
Project Editor: Joanne Rippin
Designer: Andrew Heath

Printed in China

1 3 5 7 9 10 8 6 4 2

Contents

✳

Your Garden

A garden is a lovesome thing, God wot!

(T. E. Brown "My Garden")

All gardens are different. They are different in shape and in size, they have different soils, aspects and plants. They are looked after by different people. For many families gardening is a necessary chore - the weekly mow of the lawn, an occasional foray to the garden centre to buy and plant out a few annuals to brighten the front bed - but for many more gardening is an absorbing, fascinating hobby, an endless challenge to improve the garden and grow better plants and vegetables, with the certain knowledge that if something goes wrong you will have another chance to get it right the following year.

There are two things to decide before you begin: how much time and effort do you want to put into your garden, and what do you want your garden to provide? Answering these questions will help you begin to plan your garden. Now you should put down on paper the basic shape of the garden, the principal features, the areas of bedding, vegetables and the main trees. Then look at a map and draw an arrow on your garden plan pointing south. Note also, if you have a town garden, how much of the sun gets blocked off by neighbouring houses and at which times of the day. Check the composition of your soil using a soil-testing kit.

The next stage, if you are a beginner, is to consult a good gardening book which lists plants that will grow in the conditions that you can offer them. Stick to those plants to start with. There is simply no point in trying to grow rare, tender magnolias, however much you love them, if you live in an area which has alkaline soil and low rainfall.

You may have a garden which is fully planted and requires no more than maintenance and care, you may have a new plot of land surrounded by builder's rubble, or you may have a large area of untended, neglected shrubs and trees, nettles and dandelions. All these situations present different problems. But whatever the state of your garden, it is a really good idea to keep an annual record of what you do and, if possible, to record your progress on film. That way you will know what your garden contains, and you will be able to see how it improves from year to year.

When you have decided how your garden will be used, you should draw up a detailed plan. Mark in the lawn, plot the position of any large trees and set out where the beds are or where you want them to be. Plan where your vegetable patch is to go and how big it will be.

There are various design tricks that you can use to enhance the appearance of your garden. If you have a small town patch you can make it appear longer by planting trees that are smaller as they go down the garden, or you can curve your lawn at the end to give a deeper sense of perspective. You can break up a garden into rooms, a classic concept used in many famous gardens, or you can plant hedges and trees in such a way as to lead you around corners, creating the feeling that there is always something more to discover. There are many good books available on garden design and if you want inspiration it isn't hard to find.

Left: A beautifully planted urn provides an attractive focal point in the centre of a large garden full of mature plants.
Right: A more ornamental urn blends into the foliage of a smaller-scale garden.

THE FLOWER GARDEN

The Evening Primrose opes anew
Its delicate blossoms to the dew.
And shunning hermit of the light
Wastes its fair blooms upon the night
Who blindfold to its fond caresses
Knows not the beauty it possesses.

(John Clare "The Evening Primrose")

Introduction

For most people the image conjured up by the words "flower garden" includes a cottage covered with roses and surrounded by borders of lupins, hollyhocks and delphiniums. It appeals to the romantic ideal and there is absolutely nothing wrong with this picture. However, there is rather more to a flower garden than cottage borders. Flower gardens have to be planned and for most people their garden is something they want to look at and enjoy every day of the year, not just for a few weeks each summer. That means creating a versatile framework of shrubs, roses, climbers and perennials which flower at different seasons and provide a variety of shape, size and colour.

There are some pitfalls which you should beware. If you have a tiny garden, don't be seduced into buying lovely exuberant flowering shrubs unless you have room for them. Check on the ultimate size of your plant, otherwise a few years later you will be faced with the sad task of pulling out that wonderful ceanothus that has simply grown too big for its surroundings. Also, check the aspect you can offer a plant. If it likes full sun it may not flourish in a shady town garden and if you live in the country you may not be able to provide the right shelter for plants which are not fully hardy.

It is probably best, if your garden is not too large and you don't want to be too ambitious, to devise a mixed scheme using some shrubs, some perennial plants and bulbs to flower in the spring, topped up with bedding plants and annuals for summer colour. If you plan carefully you can

aim to have some plants in flower at every season of the year, so there is always something to look at. Plant selection is the key to a successful garden.

Above: Close planting in a town garden which has been cleverly laid out to convey a wild feeling. A brick path runs around the beds and a summer house stands in the corner surrounded by mature plants. Plan your garden so that there is something happening all year round, not only for two or three months.

Trees

On a tree by a river a little tom-tit
Sang, "Willow, titwillow, titwillow!"
And I said to him, 'Dicky-bird, why do you sit
Singing, "Willow, titwillow, titwillow"?'

(W. S. Gilbert *The Mikado*)

Pink and white hawthorn in a field in late spring. This planting can be copied in many gardens to achieve the same effect.

The fortunate gardener inherits trees planted by past generations. Trees are wonderful things. They are never the same. They change from bare skeletons, shivering in the winter gales, to the fully clad green of summer, in colours ranging from the soft green, new leaves of spring to the lovely yellow, golden-orange and russet of autumn. They add shape and interest to the garden, and if by unhappy chance your new garden contains no trees, plant some as soon as you can: they will be your gift to the future.

Trees

Species		Species	
Source .... Year		Source .... Year	
Species		Species	
Source .... Year		Source .... Year	
Species		Species	
Source .... Year		Source .... Year	
Species		Species	
Source .... Year		Source .... Year	
Species		Species	
Source .... Year		Source .... Year	

The Lawn

Brushing with hasty steps the dews away
To meet the sun upon the upland lawn.
(Thomas Gray "Elegy Written in a Country Churchyard")

The lawn is probably the most important single element of the garden. There is a fashion for doing without lawns and there are many gardeners who advocate lawn-free gravel-mulched environments. On the face of it this does have its attractions, particularly in small town gardens, but even there the restful sight of a small patch of green soothes the spirit and makes the weekly mowing well worth the effort.

Lawns do need looking after. They need mowing at least once a week during the summer, possibly more in the middle of spring when the grass is growing quickly. They need feeding and weed control, autumn care to eliminate moss, and raking and spiking (aerating) in the winter or spring.

The first essential for any lawn is a mower that suits the amount of grass you have to cut. The bigger the lawn the bigger (and more expensive) the mower must be, otherwise you will spend hours just cutting the grass. It is easiest to apply fertilizer and weedkiller in liquid form and it is worth hiring (renting) a scarifier during the winter to clear out the dead thatch (grass). If you are creating a new lawn, do suit the type of seed you use to the amount of wear the lawn is going to get. Seed mixtures containing rye grass will produce a tough lawn, but if you want fine, velvety grass choose a mixture that doesn't include it. If you want to be extravagant lay good quality turf.

Large concrete paving slabs are one way of saving wear on a small lawn which has constant traffic. Make sure that the path or stepping stones are in scale with the garden otherwise they might look obtrusive.

A curving border adds interest and perspective to a lawn and gives the garden a greater feeling of depth.

Formal lawns are one of the finest features in a large garden. Here sweeping lawns lead to a Doric summerhouse flanked by beds of roses.

The Lawn

		Year	Year	Year ....
Sown	Weed/Mosskiller applied	....	....	....
Turfed	Scarified/Raked	....	....	....
	Reseeded	....	....	....
Sown	Weed/Mosskiller applied	....	....	....
Turfed	Scarified/Raked	....	....	....
	Reseeded	....	....	....

Shrubs

The rainbow comes and goes,
And lovely is the rose,
The moon doth with delight
Look round her when the heavens are bare,
Waters on a starry night
Are beautiful and fair.

(William Wordsworth "Intimations of Immortality")

Old-fashioned shrub roses make a focal point on a lawn. Unfortunately, roses are seldom grown as a shrub.

Shrubs are the mainstay of every garden. They are tolerant, undemanding and colourful, and, when established, they require little more than a mulch in the spring and - usually - some occasional pruning when they overgrow their allotted space.

Shrubs

	Year	Year	Year
Species			
.... Pruned			
Source .... Planted .... Mulched			
Species			
.... Pruned			
Source .... Planted .... Mulched			
Species			
.... Pruned			
Source .... Planted .... Mulched			
Species			
.... Pruned			
Source .... Planted .... Mulched			

Opposite: A crowded town garden with cornus, hydrangeas and teucrium interspersed with pink geraniums.

Shrubs

Species ....   Year ....   Year ....   Year ....

.... Pruned ....

Source ....   Planted ....   Mulched ....

Species ....

.... Pruned ....

Source ....   Planted ....   Mulched ....

Species ....

.... Pruned ....

Source ....   Planted ....   Mulched ....

Species ....

.... Pruned ....

Source ....   Planted ....   Mulched ....

Species ....

.... Pruned ....

Source ....   Planted ....   Mulched ....

Species ....

.... Pruned ....

Source ....   Planted ....   Mulched ....

Species ....

.... Pruned ....

Source ....   Planted ....   Mulched ....

A well-stocked and tended border within a large, old-fashioned walled garden.

Shrubs

Species ....   Year ....   Year ....   Year ....

.... Pruned ....

Source .... Planted .... Mulched ....

Species ....

.... Pruned ....

Source .... Planted .... Mulched ....

Species ....

.... Pruned ....

Source .... Planted .... Mulched ....

Massed azaleas (rhododendrons) make a striking impact if you can provide suitable soil and conditions. Many are sweetly scented.

Shrubs

		Year	Year	Year ....
Species				
....	Pruned			
Source .... Planted	Mulched			
Species				
....	Pruned			
Source .... Planted	Mulched			
Species				
....	Pruned			
Source .... Planted	Mulched			

Shrubs

Species ....   Year .... Year .... Year ....
....   Pruned   ....
Source .... Planted .... Mulched   ....

Species ....
....   Pruned   ....
Source .... Planted .... Mulched   ....

Species ....
....   Pruned   ....
Source .... Planted .... Mulched   ....

Species ....
....   Pruned   ....
Source .... Planted .... Mulched   ....

Species ....
....   Pruned   ....
Source .... Planted .... Mulched   ....

Species ....
....   Pruned   ....
Source .... Planted .... Mulched   ....

Species ....
....   Pruned   ....
Source .... Planted .... Mulched   ....

Roses

When pleasure's blooming season glows
the graces love to twine the rose.

(Edward FitzGerald "The Rubáiyát of Omar Khayyám")

In many ways roses are the best of all garden plants. They flower over a long period and some have colourful hips which last well into the autumn. They are generally hardy and the old-fashioned alba roses dating back to the Middle Ages will survive in the most difficult conditions. Roses fulfil many purposes in the garden; hybrid tea and floribunda roses are ideal for formal bedding, climbing roses cover walls and trellises, ramblers smother trees in flowers, and the old-fashioned shrub and bush roses make a focal point in any position.

Above: Summer-flowering English roses trained up a wall.

Opposite: An old-fashioned climbing rose sprawls across the wall of a tumbledown shed. All roses benefit from pruning from time to time.

Roses

			Year	Year	Year
Variety					
Type		Pruned			
Source		Mulched			
Planted		Sprayed			
Variety					
Type		Pruned			
Source		Mulched			
Planted		Sprayed			
Variety					
Type		Pruned			
Source		Mulched			
Planted		Sprayed			

Roses

Variety		Year	Year	Year
Type	Pruned			
Source	Mulched			
Planted	Sprayed			

Variety				
Type	Pruned			
Source	Mulched			
Planted	Sprayed			

Variety				
Type	Pruned			
Source	Mulched			
Planted	Sprayed			

Variety				
Type	Pruned			
Source	Mulched			
Planted	Sprayed			

Variety				
Type	Pruned			
Source	Mulched			
Planted	Sprayed			

Herbaceous Plants

And the jessamine faint and the sweet tuberose,
The sweetest flower for scent that blows.
(Percy Bysshe Shelley "The Sensitive Plant")

A well-kept lawn and tidy herbaceous border leads to a more untamed area to create an attractive contrast.

There is little in a garden more satisfying than an old-fashioned herbaceous border in high summer. A herbaceous border may take some planning, but with a little effort it will provide continuous colour and interest from early spring through to the autumn. Once established it only requires staking, routine maintenance and tidying up in the autumn and spring. Lupins, hollyhocks, delphiniums, clumps of hardy geraniums, bleeding hearts, tradescantia, evening primrose, fuchsias, asters, anemones and astilbes are just a few of the plants that can be blended together to make a colourful display. Before you start planing, plan your border on paper, paying particular attention to the tallest plants which should be placed at the back.

Herbaceous Plants

Species		Year	Year	Year
Source	Mulched			
Planted	Divided/Propagated			
Species				
Source	Mulched			
Planted	Divided/Propagated			
Species				
Source	Mulched			
Planted	Divided/Propagated			

Herbaceous Plants

Species .... Year .... Year .... Year ....

Source .... Mulched ....
Planted .... Divided/Propagated ....

Species ....

Source .... Mulched ....
Planted .... Divided/Propagated ....

Species ....

Source .... Mulched ....
Planted .... Divided/Propagated ....

Species ....

Source .... Mulched ....
Planted .... Divided/Propagated ....

Species ....

Source .... Mulched ....
Planted .... Divided/Propagated ....

Herbaceous Plants

Species		Year	Year	Year
Source	Mulched			
Planted	Divided/Propagated			
Species				
Source	Mulched			
Planted	Divided/Propagated			
Species				
Source	Mulched			
Planted	Divided/Propagated			

A handsome town house is enhanced by a beautifully balanced front garden.

A garden pool surrounded by an eye-catching combination of plants: foxgloves, Solomon's seal, irises and honeysuckle frame the water-lilies floating on the water.

Climbers

Fain would I climb, yet fear I to fall.
If thy heart fails thee, climb not at all.
(attributed to Sir Walter Raleigh and Elizabeth I)

Climbers are one of the best ways to extend a small garden upwards. They cover the walls in flowers and obscure unsightly fences.

Wisteria is one of the loveliest climbers of all in early summer.

Climbers

	Year	Year	Year
Species			
Source			
Planted			
Pruned			
Mulched			
Species			
Source			
Planted			
Pruned			
Mulched			
Species			
Source			
Planted			
Pruned			
Mulched			
Species			
Source			
Planted			
Pruned			
Mulched			

Climbers

Species ....   Year ....   Year ....   Year ....

Source ....   Pruned   ....
Planted ....   Mulched   ....

Species ....

Source ....   Pruned   ....
Planted ....   Mulched   ....

Species ....

Source ....   Pruned   ....
Planted ....   Mulched   ....

Species ....

Source ....   Pruned   ....
Planted ....   Mulched   ....

Species ....

Source ....   Pruned   ....
Planted ....   Mulched   ....

Bulbs & Tubers

... a crowd,
A host, of golden daffodils;
Beside the lake, beneath the trees,
Fluttering and dancing in the breeze.
(William Wordsworth "I Wandered Lonely as a Cloud")

The bulbs of spring are one of the first signs that the wheel of the seasons has turned and that warmer summer days are on their way. There is something particularly charming about these early flowers, the yellow of the winter aconites, the nodding heads of the snowdrops and the upright crocuses which flirt with the sun, opening their heads to receive its rays then closing up when it goes behind the clouds. Daffodils and narcissus are the most spectacular bulbs, covering gardens with yellow fields of colour. But there are also summer bulbs such as lilies, galtonias, scillas and chionodoxas, all of which have a place in the garden. Then there are also the tubers, gladioli, begonias and, most important of all, the dahlias which have their own separate section in this book.

Above: A garden shed is given a new lease of life with a coat of paint and some decorative pots.

Opposite: Hyacinths, one of the best loved and popular bulbs, often grown as gifts at Christmas time as a foretaste of the coming spring.

Bulbs & Tubers

Species		Year	Year	Year
Source	Fed			
Planted	Divided			
Species				
Source	Fed			
Planted	Divided			

The last flowers of the narcissi are succeeded by carpets of bluebells in a woodland ride in early summer.

Bulbs & Tubers

Species					Year	Year	Year
Source		Fed					
Planted		Divided					
Species							
Source		Fed					
Planted		Divided					
Species							
Source		Fed					
Planted		Divided					

Bulbs & Tubers

Species ....

	Year	Year	Year

Source .... Fed

Planted .... Divided

Species ....

Source .... Fed

Planted .... Divided

Species ....

Source .... Fed

Planted .... Divided

Species ....

Source .... Fed

Planted .... Divided

Species ....

Source .... Fed

Planted .... Divided

Dahlias

It is a frost! - the dahlias are dead!

(R. S. Surtees *Handley Cross*)

The fresh yellow flowers of the 'Margareth' dahlia. When grown in borders dahlias will need staking.

Dahlias are one of the most rewarding plants to grow. There are ten main divisions which correspond to the flower types, and as many as 31 subdivisions, producing flowers of many colours and shapes. The tubers should be planted out in the spring, and then dug up and stored when the first frosts cut down the flowers in the autumn. Remember to label the tubers when you dig them up, then allow them to dry out.

Dahlias

			Year	Year	Year
Source					
Planted	Planted out	Lifted			
Source					
Planted	Planted out	Lifted			
Source					
Planted	Planted out	Lifted			
Source					
Planted	Planted out	Lifted			
Source					
Planted	Planted out	Lifted			
Source					
Planted	Planted out	Lifted			

Annuals & Bedding Plants

... there is pansies, that's for thoughts.
(William Shakespeare *Hamlet*)

Annuals and bedding plants provide instant colour in the garden. They brighten the summer in towns and cities all over the world, enlivening tubs (planters) and window-boxes, and if you have room they are well worth planting in a bed on their own or among the permanent plants in the herbaceous or mixed border.

Use co-ordinating pots and ornaments to create a themed corner in your garden, as with this Chinese collection.

Annuals & Bedding Plants

Species ....

Sown .... Planted out ....

Species ....

Sown .... Planted out ....

Species ....

Sown .... Planted out ....

Species ....

Sown .... Planted out ....

Species ....

Sown .... Planted out ....

Species ....

Sown .... Planted out ....

Species ....

Sown .... Planted out ....

Species ....

Sown .... Planted out ....

Annuals and bedding plants are often used to fill in the gaps in a border of more established plants.

Annuals & Bedding Plants

Species ....

Sown .... Planted out ....

Species ....

Sown .... Planted out ....

Species ....

Sown .... Planted out ....

Species ....

Sown .... Planted out ....

Species ....

Sown .... Planted out ....

Species ....

Sown .... Planted out ....

Species ....

Sown .... Planted out ....

Here a window-box is used to stunning effect with a colour-coordinated display of bedding plants.

Thyme, in flower here, makes a good edge for a border, and when the weather is sunny it emits a lovely, heady scent.

Annuals & Bedding Plants

Species ....

Sown .... Planted out ....

Species ....

Sown .... Planted out ....

Species ....

Sown .... Planted out ....

Species ....

Sown .... Planted out ....

Species ....

Sown .... Planted out ....

Species ....

Sown .... Planted out ....

A dense display of foliage and flowering plants with a pleasing and original mix of colours and textures.

Species ....

Sown .... Planted out ....

Species ....

Sown .... Planted out ....

Species ....

Sown .... Planted out ....

Species ....

Sown .... Planted out ....

Species ....

Sown .... Planted out ....

Species ....

Sown .... Planted out ....

THE KITCHEN GARDEN

Oh, Adam was a gardener, and God who made him sees
That half a proper gardener's work is done upon his knees,
So when your work is finished, you can wash your hands
and pray
For the Glory of the Garden, that it may not pass away!
And the Glory of the Garden it shall never pass away!

(Rudyard Kipling "The Glory of the Garden")

Shallots are easy to grow and will add a touch of class and originality to your cooking.

Introduction

For many gardeners the kitchen garden is the hub of the year's activities. It is perfectly possible, even with a fairly small vegetable plot, to keep a family of two adults and three children in vegetables for at least eight months of the year. With careful planning and a certain amount of deep-freezing a family need spend very little money on buying vegetables at all. When you see the prices charged for vegetables in most supermarkets, the saving - for the cost of a few packets of seeds and a little hard work - is well worth having. One gardening commentator said that digging was better exercise than jogging and at the end of it you had a nice looking patch of good brown earth. He may not be correct medically, but it is a sentiment that all enthusiastic gardeners would agree with wholeheartedly.

The important thing is to plan the kitchen garden at the start of the year so that the vegetables follow in succession. It really is worth sowing seeds at fortnightly (biweekly) intervals throughout the summer and planning to grow winter vegetables - Brussels sprouts, winter cabbage, winter broccoli and spring greens - to eat when the glut of summer vegetables is over. You need a good supply of organic matter, preferably well-rotted manure, to dig into the soil when one crop is over before replanting with another. You also need to be determined to defeat the birds as they descend on the tender emerging shoots. It is a good deal easier to grow peas in the centre of a city, where the multitudes of pigeons are used to feeding on scraps and are completely uneducated about fresh vegetables, than in the depths of the country.

Finally there is the question of flavour: there is absolutely nothing so good as fresh young vegetables picked and cooked straight from the garden, while the fact that you have grown them yourself makes the pleasure of eating them even greater.

Vegetables

Then a sentimental passion of a vegetable fashion
must excite your languid spleen,
An attachment à la Plato, for a bashful young potato,
or a not too French French bean!

(W. S. Gilbert *Patience*)

There is absolutely nothing so good as fresh young vegetables, and the fact that they have been grown and freshly picked by you makes the pleasure of eating them that much greater. Those Arran Pilot early potatoes, and new sugar snap peas cooked in the pod, young asparagus in the spring, ping-pong ball-sized beetroot, all quite delicious and immeasurably superior to anything you might buy at the supermarket.

A pile of home-grown vegetables will inspire any cook and tempt any appetite.

Vegetables

		Year	Year	Year ....
Vegetable	Sown	....	....	....
Variety	Thinned	....	....	....
	Harvested	....	....	....
Vegetable	Sown	....	....	....
Variety	Thinned	....	....	....
	Harvested	....	....	....
Vegetable	Sown	....	....	....
Variety	Thinned	....	....	....
	Harvested	....	....	....
Vegetable	Sown	....	....	....
Variety	Thinned	....	....	....
	Harvested	....	....	....

Vegetables

	Year	Year	Year ....
Vegetable .... Sown	....	....	....
Variety .... Thinned	....	....	....
Harvested	....	....	....
Vegetable .... Sown	....	....	....
Variety .... Thinned	....	....	....
Harvested	....	....	....
Vegetable .... Sown	....	....	....
Variety .... Thinned	....	....	....
Harvested	....	....	....
Vegetable .... Sown	....	....	....
Variety .... Thinned	....	....	....
Harvested	....	....	....

Above: Fine carrots fit for a greengrocer's shelf. The best carrots are pulled when they are half this size and cooked with butter and a little sugar.

Opposite: A breathtaking display of produce in a large and well cared for country kitchen garden.

A fine, large vegetable garden with beetroot, spinach and broad beans. If you have the room it is a good idea, as here, to grow sweet peas in the vegetable garden for cutting.

Above: The vegetable garden at the Royal Horticultural Society at Wisley, England. Artichokes are fine decorative plants but need plenty of room to flourish.

Right: A wonderful old wooden wheelbarrow, as much an ornamental feature as it is a gardening tool.

Vegetables

	Year	Year	Year
Vegetable	Sown		
Variety	Thinned		
	Harvested		
Vegetable	Sown		
Variety	Thinned		
	Harvested		
Vegetable	Sown		
Variety	Thinned		
	Harvested		
Vegetable	Sown		
Variety	Thinned		
	Harvested		

Vegetables

		Year	Year	Year
Vegetable	Sown			
Variety	Thinned			
	Harvested			
Vegetable	Sown			
Variety	Thinned			
	Harvested			
Vegetable	Sown			
Variety	Thinned			
	Harvested			
Vegetable	Sown			
Variety	Thinned			
	Harvested			

An allotment garden with a 4 ft (1.2 m) bed system, where crops are sown in succession.

An old-fashioned scarecrow guarding a rather untamed garden.

Even quite ramshackle greenhouses, such as this one, in need of considerable attention, can still be used to raise early lettuces.

Vegetables

		Year	Year	Year ....
Vegetable	Sown			
Variety	Thinned			
	Harvested			
Vegetable	Sown			
Variety	Thinned			
	Harvested			
Vegetable	Sown			
Variety	Thinned			
	Harvested			
Vegetable	Sown			
Variety	Thinned			
	Harvested			

Herbs

There's rosemary, that's for remembrance; pray, love, remember:

(William Shakespeare *Hamlet*)

Try to find some room in your garden to grow a few herbs. No cook should be without a supply of fresh mint, parsley, rosemary, chives and thyme, and, if you are more ambitious, tarragon, basil and coriander (cilantro). Don't be put off growing herbs for lack of space, you can always use a pot or a window-box.

Fresh herbs for the kitchen make any savoury dish taste that much better.

Herbs

		Year	Year	Year
Type	Sown			
Variety	Thinned			
Type	Sown			
Variety	Thinned			
Type	Sown			
Variety	Thinned			
Type	Sown			
Variety	Thinned			
Type	Sown			
Variety	Thinned			
Type	Sown			
Variety	Thinned			
Type	Sown			
Variety	Thinned			

Opposite: A fine herb garden with the herbs grown in individual borders edged with planking and immaculate gravel.

Herbs

		Year	Year	Year
Type	Sown	....	....	....
Variety	Thinned	....	....	....
Type	Sown	....	....	....
Variety	Thinned	....	....	....
Type	Sown	....	....	....
Variety	Thinned	....	....	....
Type	Sown	....	....	....
Variety	Thinned	....	....	....

A selection of herbs in small individual pots, these are just the right size for planting together in a large pot. Make sure there is enough room for them to grow.

Fruit

Go, bind thou up yon dangling apricocks,
Which, like unruly children, make their sire
Stoop with oppression of their prodigal weight.

(William Shakespeare *King Richard II*)

If you have space in your garden, do consider growing some fruit. This may present a challenge: to grow fruit successfully you need either plenty of space or a garden that doesn't have to double as a playing field. If you have children and a small town garden, don't plant raspberry canes (vines) or espalier apple trees along the walls: the football will do too much damage to make the effort worthwhile. But if you don't have any such obstacles you can certainly grow raspberries up a wall, or espalier apple and pear trees along the fence. There are many excellent varieties available grafted on to miniature rootstocks for this purpose.

If you do have room you can make a fruit cage in which to grow strawberries and raspberries. You can plant currant (berry) bushes, apple, pear and plum trees and if you live in a mild enough climate and have a south or south-west facing wall you can try growing peaches or apricots. With the help of the freezer you can again make major inroads into the family's expenditure at the supermarket. But beware of the birds: you will need to net all your fruit or the birds will get the lot before you can.

Strawberries epitomize the long warm days of early summer and can be grown in containers as well as in the ground.

Fruit Trees

		Year	Year	Year ....
Type	Planted			
Variety	Pruned			
Source	Mulched			
	Sprayed			
	Picked			
Type	Planted			
Variety	Pruned			
Source	Mulched			
	Sprayed			
	Picked			
Type	Planted			
Variety	Pruned			
Source	Mulched			
	Sprayed			
	Picked			
Type	Planted			
Variety	Pruned			
Source	Mulched			
	Sprayed			
	Picked			

Soft Fruit & Currants

		Year	Year	Year ....
Type	Planted	....	....	....
Variety	Pruned	....	....	....
Source	Mulched	....	....	....
	Sprayed	....	....	....
	Picked	....	....	....
Type	Planted	....	....	....
Variety	Pruned	....	....	....
Source	Mulched	....	....	....
	Sprayed	....	....	....
	Picked	....	....	....
Type	Planted	....	....	....
Variety	Pruned	....	....	....
Source	Mulched	....	....	....
	Sprayed	....	....	....
	Picked	....	....	....

Make the most of a plentiful harvest by bottling and preserving your fruit.

The Greenhouse

A considerable number of my tasks when I started in the gardens were confined to the greenhouses. These consisted of six vineries, six peach houses, two large plant houses and two small growing houses.

(*Ted Humphris* Garden Glory)

Introduction

A good greenhouse is of enormous help to the serious gardener, and even a small one is well worth having. It prolongs the growing season as seeds can be started earlier in the warmer, frost-free atmosphere under glass. It enables the gardener to grow indoor tomatoes, cucumbers, peppers, aubergines (eggplants), melons and even grapes, and it can also provide flowers at Christmas. It makes it much easier to take cuttings to increase your stock of plants and overwinter tender summer bedding plants. It does take planning, care and

diligence to manage all this, and, if you want to grow exotic plants, the greenhouse must be heated. A greenhouse requires a good deal of attention, especially during the winter when the atmosphere must be as dry as possible. It is essential to pay attention to ventilation throughout the year and in winter you need to adjust the heating according to the type of plant you are trying to grow.

Above: Greenhouses come in all shapes and sizes, this is a very modern design.

Seeds

The sower went forth sowing,
The seed in secret slept.

(W. St Hill Bourne *Church Bells* "The Sower Went Forth Sowing")

Most people use their greenhouse to raise plants from seeds. This is the most satisfactory way of raising vegetables, annuals and biennials. It is also the cheapest and, as there are always seeds to spare, you can exchange any that are left over with friends. Sow the seed as thinly as possible, keep a careful record of those sown and label the trays clearly.

If your seeds fail, you can usually buy replacement seedlings from a commercial greenhouse or garden centre.

Seeds

	Year	Year	Year
Type .... Sown	....	....	....
Variety .... Planted out	....	....	....
Type .... Sown	....	....	....
Variety .... Planted out	....	....	....
Type .... Sown	....	....	....
Variety .... Planted out	....	....	....
Type .... Sown	....	....	....
Variety .... Planted out	....	....	....
Type .... Sown	....	....	....
Variety .... Planted out	....	....	....
Type .... Sown	....	....	....
Variety .... Planted out	....	....	....

Cuttings

There is no ancient gentlemen but gardeners, ditchers, and
gravemakers; they hold up Adam's profession.
(William Shakespeare *Hamlet*)

It is relatively easy to raise new plants by taking cuttings. Pelargoniums, clematis and many shrubs can be
raised from softwood or semiripe cuttings taken in
spring and summer. Other trees and shrubs can be raised
from hardwood cuttings that are taken in autumn.
Chrysanthemum cuttings can be taken in the greenhouse
in winter. Many cuttings can also be grown in a jar of
water on the kitchen window-sill.

Rooted cuttings ready for planting out in position in spring.

Cuttings

		Year	Year	Year
Plant	Taken			
	Planted out			
Plant	Taken			
	Planted out			
Plant	Taken			
	Planted out			
Plant	Taken			
	Planted out			
Plant	Taken			
	Planted out			
Plant	Taken			
	Planted out			

Vegetables & Tomatoes

The luscious clusters of the vine
Upon my mouth do crush their wine;
The nectarine and the curious peach,
Into my hands themselves do reach;
Stumbling on melons, as I pass
Insnar'd with flow'rs, I fall on grass.
(Andrew Marvell "The Garden")

Cuttings raised in a cold frame.

Many gardeners use their greenhouse to raise greenhouse tomatoes and grow some early vegetables from seed. But for the more adventurous, there are a number of other, more exotic, possibilities, such as cucumbers, aubergines (eggplants), melons and, if there is enough room, indoor vines or the delicate varieties of stone fruit trees such as peaches and nectarines.

Vegetables & Tomatoes

		Year	Year	Year ....
Type	Sown	....	....	....
Variety	Planted out	....	....	....
	Harvested	....	....	....
Type	Sown	....	....	....
Variety	Planted out	....	....	....
	Harvested	....	....	....
Type	Sown	....	....	....
Variety	Planted out	....	....	....
	Harvested	....	....	....

Vegetables

	Year	Year	Year
Type			
Sown			
Variety			
Planted out			
Harvested			

Type			
Sown			
Variety			
Planted out			
Harvested			

Type			
Sown			
Variety			
Planted out			
Harvested			

Type			
Sown			
Variety			
Planted out			
Harvested			

Type			
Sown			
Variety			
Planted out			
Harvested			

Type			
Sown			
Variety			
Planted out			
Harvested			

Opposite: Young plants growing in the cold frame of a greenhouse of a large country estate.

Flowers, Bulbs & Tubers

The painted tulip in her bloom begun
Opens her splendid bosom to the sun
The tempted bee hums round with amorous gaze
And in her magic beauty toys and plays.

(John Clare "The Tulip and the Bee")

Greenhouse flowers are a bit special. For most people they mean early bulbs, hyacinths, narcissus and crocuses specially prepared for forcing, which can be bought in the autumn, kept in the dark, then brought into the light to flower from Christmas onwards.

Another favourite greenhouse bulb is the showy amaryllis or hippeastrum, and the clivias with its lovely orange and yellow trumpets of flowers in the spring. A greenhouse will see many flowers pass through it as cuttings or tubers or as plants in pots. It is a great addition to any garden.

Use your greenhouse to bring on flowers which you can then use to augment your garden displays, like this lovely patio arrangement.

Flowers, Bulbs & Tubers

		Year	Year	Year
Species	Planted/Sown			
	Planted out			
	Flowered			
Species	Planted/Sown			
	Planted out			
	Flowered			
Species	Planted/Sown			
	Planted out			
	Flowered			
Species	Planted/Sown			
	Planted out			
	Flowered			
Species	Planted/Sown			
	Planted out			
	Flowered			
Species	Planted/Sown			
	Planted out			
	Flowered			

Weather

Here shall he see
No enemy
But winter and rough weather
(William Shakespeare *As You Like It*)

Remember to feed the birds during cold weather,
some may be depending on you to help them through the winter.

All gardeners, like all farmers, grumble about the weather and often with very good reason. To give some substance to these grumbles, it is of interest to note the main details of the weather each year. There are two good instruments which anyone can use. The first is a maximum/minimum thermometer. Place this on a north-facing wall and note the temperature, either each day, or in extremes of heat or cold. For instance, if you know that for 16 consecutive days in the winter the temperature did not rise above freezing-point, it will not surprise you to find that a number of plants have died when spring arrives.

Weather Year

	Rainfall	Sunshine	Average Temperature	Comments
January				
February				
March				
April				
May				
June				
July				
August				
September				
October				
November				
December				

Weather Year ....

	Rainfall	Sunshine	Average Temperature	Comments
January				
February				
March				
April				
May				
June				
July				
August				
September				
October				
November				
December				

Weather Year ....

	Rainfall	Sunshine	Average Temperature	Comments
January				
February				
March				
April				
May				
June				
July				
August				
September				
October				
November				
December				

Tools & Machinery

Tools & Machinery

Lawnmower	Guarantee ....
Supplier	
Telephone No.	Serviced ....
Rotavator	Guarantee ....
Supplier	
Telephone No.	Serviced ....
Other Machines	Guarantee ....
Supplier	
Telephone No.	Serviced ....

Plant Suppliers

Plant Suppliers

Name ....

Address ....
....

Telephone No. ....

The pretty violet-blue flowers of a geranium.

Name ....

Address ....
....

Telephone No. ....

Name ....

Address ....
....

Telephone No. ....

Name ....

Address ....
....

Telephone No. ....

Name ....

Address ....
....

Telephone No. ....